CW00429046

Other titles in this series:
The Victim's Guide to Air Travel
The Victim's Guide to the Baby
The Victim's Guide to the Dentist
The Victim's Guide to the Doctor
The Victim's Guide to Middle Age

Published simultaneously in 1994 by Exley Publications in Great Britain, and Exley Giftbooks in the USA.

ISBN 1-85015-504-6

A copy of the CIP data is available from the British Library on request.

Printed in Spain by Grafo, S.A. Bilbao.

Exley Publications Ltd, 16 Chalk Hill, Watford, Herts WD1 4BN, UK.
Exley Giftbooks, 232 Madison Avenue, Suite 1206, New York, NY 10016, USA.

THE VICTIM'S GUIDE TO ...

EXLEY
NEW YORK • WATFORD, UK

Christmas comes but once a year, but even this is too much for some people....

CHRISTMAS IS COMING! CHRISTMAS IS COMING!

CHRISTMAS IS COMING, READY OR NOT!

Christmas shopping can be a nightmare....

I THOUGHT I HEARD A SCREAM!
(apologies to Edvard Munch)

GIFTS

Merry
Christmas

SUPER
CHRISTMAS
SALE

And then there are all the other
Christmas necessities....

I'M SURE HE WASN'T THERE WHEN WE BOUGHT THE TREE!

WISE MEN DO NOT CHEW GUM, DARREN!

HE DID IT AGAIN, MISS!

It is so important to choose just the right gift,
just the right card....

For the man who has everything

Merry
Christmas
Darling xx

OH, DEAR—NO NAME ON THIS ONE — I WONDER WHO IT'S FOR!
Merry Christmas you old Grump xx

GREETIN
I WANT A CARD FOR SOMEONE WHO DOESN'T LIKE CHRISTMAS!

HE'S GOT A LITTLE LIST!
(Apologies to Gilbert & Sullivan)

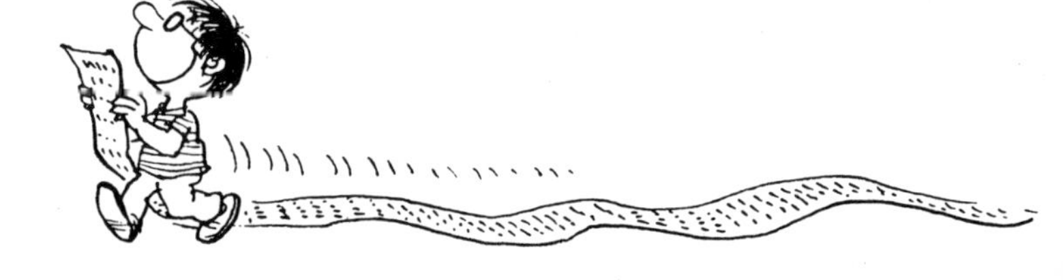

OF COURSE IT LOOKS FAMILIAR—
IT'S THE ONE WE GAVE HER LAST YEAR!
Happy Christmas from Aunt Flo.

MERRY XMAS
BEER
Fiddy.

I STILL DON'T FEEL CHRISTMASSY!
Fiddy

HE'S HAD A GREAT IDEA. HE'S GOING TO HANG UP A QUILT COVER THIS YEAR!
Fiddes

COMPLAINTS
10,000 Pieces
JIGSAW
LUDO
Fiddy

Christmas is a time to be together,
a time of good will to all men.....

MERRY CHRISTMAS !!

HEY! ARE YOU ALL DEAF ?— I SAID MERRY CHRISTMAS!

WITH CARE
TOMATO KETCHUP
THIS WAY UP
Merry
XMAS
HAPPY CHRIST MAS
Merry

I WISH YOU A
MERRY CHRISTMAS AND
A HAPPY NEW
YEAR

Best Wishes
for Christmas

CHRISTMAS
GREETINGS

MERRY
CHRISTMAS

Christmas
Cheer

Happy
Christmas!

Merry
Xmas

Nöel
Nöel

Seasons
Greetings

Happy New
Year!

Happy
New
Year

JOYEUX
NOEL

ALL I SAID WAS I THINK I'D PREFER FRUIT SALAD!
Fiddes

GEORGE IS THE LIFE AND SOUL OF THE PARTY, JOAN — COULD YOU PLEASE TAKE HIM HOME ?

6
5
4
3
2
1

PURR
PURR
PURR
PURR
Fiddy

Christmas is the festive season, a time
for family and friends, peace and love.....

IT'S PARTY TIME!!

Roland Fiddy

Dog attempting to send a telepathic message to his master.

ZZZZZ

QUIET EVERYBODY—
GRANDAD IS GOING
TO DO HIS TRICK!

MICE DON'T USE SPOONS!
Fiddy

Jingle Bells
Jingle Bells
Jingle Bells
Jingle Bells
Jingle Bells
Jingle Bells
Jingle Bells
Jingle Bells
JAN
8

WE SENT THEM THAT CARD THREE YEARS AGO!

THEY HAD 64 CARDS —WE HAVE 73!

However, most people do their best to enter into the spirit of Christmas, however reluctantly....

Of course, children love Santa Claus ....

IT'S HALF PAST ONE AND SANTA CLAUS STILL HASN'T COME!

HE DID COME!
HE DID COME!
HE DID COME!

THAT'S FUNNY— YOUR SHOES ARE JUST LIKE MY DADDY'S!

YOU'D BETTER TAKE OFF THE BEARD!

ALL RIGHT, THEN— I DON'T BELIEVE IN YOU EITHER!
FIDDES

HE'S THE LITTLE BOY THAT SANTA CLAUS WANTED TO FORGET.

2

THWACK!

3

YOUR "HO, HO, HO!" ISN'T
VERY CONVINCING!

Fiddy

OH! OH! OH!

CHEER UP—HALF OF IT IS PROBABLY JUNK MAIL!
MAIL
MAIL
MAIL
MAIL

Ho!Ho!Ho!Ho!Ho!Ho!
Ho!Ho Ho!Ho!Ho!Ho!

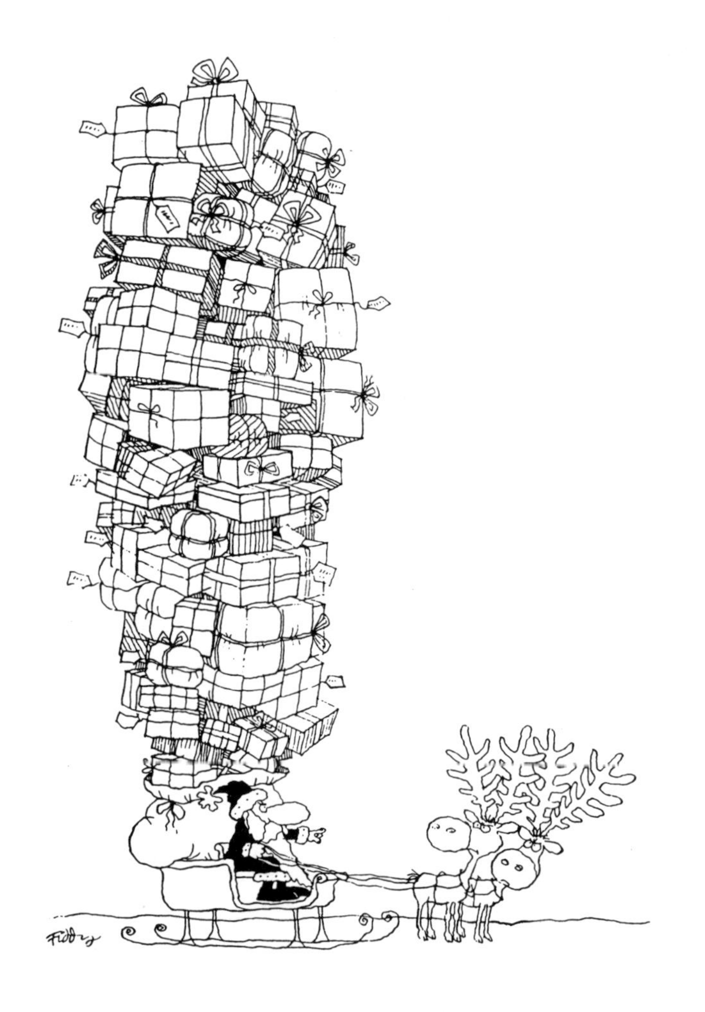

I HATE
CHRISTMAS

TOUGH NIGHT, DEAR?

ONLY 364 SHOPPING DAYS TO CHRISTMAS
PRICES SLASHED —!

Books in the "Victim's Guide" series
($4.99 £2.99 paperback)

Award-winning cartoonist Roland Fiddy sees the funny side of life's phobias, nightmares and catastrophes.

The Victim's Guide to Air Travel
The Victim's Guide to the Baby
The Victim's Guide to Christmas
The Victim's Guide to the Dentist
The Victim's Guide to the Doctor
The Victim's Guide to Middle Age

The "Fanatic's" series
($4.99 £2.99)

The **Fanatic's Guides** are perfect presents for everyone with a hobby that has got out of hand. Eighty pages of hilarious black and white cartoons by Roland Fiddy.

The Fanatic's Guide to the Bed
The Fanatic's Guide to Cats
The Fanatic's Guide to Computers
The Fanatic's Guide to Dads
The Fanatic's Guide to Diets
The Fanatic's Guide to Dogs
The Fanatic's Guide to Husbands
The Fanatic's Guide to Money
The Fanatic's Guide to Sex
The Fanatic's Guide to Skiing

Books in the "Crazy World" series
($4.99 £2.99 paperback)

The Crazy World of Aerobics (Bill Stott)
The Crazy World of Cats (Bill Stott)
The Crazy World of Cricket (Bill Stott)
The Crazy World of Gardening (Bill Stott)
The Crazy World of Golf (Mike Scott)
The Crazy World of the Greens (Barry Knowles)
The Crazy World of the Handyman (Bill Stott)
The Crazy World of Hospitals (Bill Stott)
The Crazy World of Housework (Bill Stott)
The Crazy World of the Learner Driver (Bill Stott)
The Crazy World of Love (Roland Fiddy)
The Crazy World of Marriage (Bill Stott)
The Crazy World of Rugby (Bill Stott)
The Crazy World of Sailing (Peter Rigby)
The Crazy World of Sex (David Pye)
The Crazy World of Soccer (Bill Stott)

Books in the "Mini Joke Book" series
($6.99 £3.99 hardback)

These attractive 64 page mini joke books are illustrated throughout by Bill Stott.

A Binge of Diet Jokes
A Bouquet of Wedding Jokes
A Feast of After Dinner Jokes
A Knockout of Sports Jokes
A Portfolio of Business Jokes
A Round of Golf Jokes
A Romp of Naughty Jokes
A Spread of Over-40s Jokes
A Tankful of Motoring Jokes

Great Britain: Order these super books from your local bookseller or From Exley Publications Ltd, 16 Chalk Hill, Watford, Herts WDl 4BN. Please send £1.30 to cover post and packaging on 1 book, £2.60 on 2 or more books.)